Balanced ~~BUSY~~ LIFE Journal

Creating Daily Habits for the
"Perfect" Work-Life Blance

WELCOME

Welcome My Friend,

I am so glad you have decided to take this journey with me to create new habits for our lives. This is where we will strive for productivity over perfection and better over busy. Here, we will set daily goals to experience greater joy and focus on the areas that matter.

How can we learn to embrace our now season while fully preparing for our next season? The answer to this question can be summed up in the word "balance."

What is balance?

Balance is not a perfect day or a checked-off to-do list. It is a productive day full of priceless memories with daily and eternal significance. That is why this journal was created—to pull you toward the important things of life, not away from them.

You will see this journal is broken down into seven categories on a plate. Why a plate? Because I truly believe when we change the perspective of the word, "busy" to "My plate is full," it helps us to better consider the weight of the tasks we take on.

Here is what I mean.

Take a moment and visualize your Thanksgiving or Christmas plate (this is a judgment-free moment so no worries). For instance, mine is usually a large plate overflowing with delicious, tasty, good food I tend to only consume once, maybe twice a year. Now let's get back to visualizing your plate. As you indulge in the food one bite at a time, the plate becomes emptier and your stomach gets fuller. You have now lessened the items on your plate, but as you have done so you exchanged them for an overwhelmingly full stomach. It is at that moment you realize no matter how good the food is, no matter where it is (on the plate or in your stomach) it is simply too much.

I know you are probably thinking, what does this have to do with being busy. Everything, my friend! That plate represents your busy life. Your choice to fill it up until it is brimming or portion it out determines how you will feel in the end. The full plate looks amazing but when it becomes a full stomach, it doesn't always feel so great. Every yes is another piece of food added to the plate that will have to be consumed into your already full stomach. That, my friend, is what busy looks and feels like.

Changing the terminology from "I am busy," to "My plate is full," has helped me to take better inventory of my commitments, time, and responsibilities. I consider what has to be on my plate and what can be removed so I can enjoy the experience of life.

When people say, "Rachel, you're so busy," I correct them and say, "Well, my plate is a bit full right now, but I'm removing things slowly but surely." Or if they say, "I know you're busy but…" I respond by saying, "Let me see what's on my plate." Busy doesn't give me the visual I need to really pause and take everything into consideration.

Sure, I've had some tough conversations and said "no" to things I really wanted to say "yes" to. However, when I think of the damage I was doing to the best version of myself by not taking inventory of what was on my plate and constantly adding more items, I knew it was worth it.

It is my goal that as we work through this journal, our new perspective will create new experiences for us.

So let's get started!

Here is how it works:

Each day, you will be given space to write one thing you will accomplish in six key areas and a truth for you to meditate on throughout your day. Here are the key areas you will focus on:

Myself: What is one thing you will do today for yourself? Read a book, take a nap, go for a run, take a calm bubble bath, play an instrument, etc.

My Loved Ones: What is one thing you will do with your family? Play a game, watch a movie, read to your children, go for a walk, do a fire pit, have a Bible study, listen to music, write a song, etc.

My Community: How can your imprint be a part of building your community today? Praying for your leaders, serving in the community, serving at church, sharing with the youth, helping your neighbor, etc.

My Work: What is one task you have to get done, need to start, or must complete today? Finish a project, send important responses, call a client, balance the books, etc.

My Future: What will you do today to set yourself up for long-term or short-term success? Take an online program, meet with an accountability partner, send a pitch for your speaking engagement, submit for a guest podcast, sit with a mentor, etc.

My Finances: How will you be accountable for your financial portfolio, present and future today? Check your bank account, schedule your bill transfers, move money to savings, make calls about your credit, put money aside for retirement, etc.

My Truth for the Day: What is one truth you will use to encourage you throughout the day? This can be an inspirational quote, Scripture verse, family mantra, encouraging text, etc.

For each of these areas, as difficult as it may be, choose only one task per area per day. This will take some training and self-control but you can do it. Remember, balance isn't about spending equal amounts of time on every task. Rather, it is spending the right amount of time on the right tasks.

Your Friend,

Rachel G. Scott

Writer | Speaker | Founder of I Can't Come Down Movement

Special Note: As I write this, I want to be fully transparent and say I am a student of this teaching as I am learning to implement these new habits in my own life. So let's agree to use this journal as a place of intentionality and growth and not guilt and shame. Some days will go better than others but our motives and intentions will remain the same, to balance our platters so we can focus on what matters.

Date: ___/___/___

For Myself

For My Loved Ones

For My Community

For My Work

For My Future

For My Finances

My Truth for the Day

Date: ___/___/___

For Myself

For My Loved Ones

For My Community

For My Work

For My Future

For My Finances

My Truth for the Day

Date: ___/___/___

For Myself

For My Loved Ones

For My Community

For My Work

For My Future

For My Finances

My Truth for the Day

Date: ___/___/___

For Myself

For My Loved Ones

For My Community

For My Work

For My Future

For My Finances

My Truth for the Day

Date: ___/___/___

For Myself

For My Loved Ones

For My Community

For My Work

For My Future

For My Finances

My Truth for the Day

Date: ___/___/___

For Myself

For My Loved Ones

For My Community

For My Work

For My Future

For My Finances

My Truth for the Day

Date: ___/___/___

For Myself

For My Loved Ones

For My Community

For My Work

For My Future

For My Finances

My Truth for the Day

Date: ___/___/___

For Myself

For My Loved Ones

For My Community

For My Work

For My Future

For My Finances

My Truth for the Day

Date: ___/___/___

For Myself

For My Loved Ones

For My Community

For My Work

For My Future

For My Finances

My Truth for the Day

Date: ___/___/___

For Myself

For My Loved Ones

For My Community

For My Work

For My Future

For My Finances

My Truth for the Day

Date: ___/___/___

For Myself

For My Loved Ones

For My Community

For My Work

For My Future

For My Finances

My Truth for the Day

Date: ___/___/___

For Myself

For My Loved Ones

For My Community

For My Work

For My Future

For My Finances

My Truth for the Day

Date: ___/___/___

For Myself

For My Loved Ones

For My Community

For My Work

For My Future

For My Finances

My Truth for the Day

Date: ___/___/___

For Myself

For My Loved Ones

For My Community

For My Work

For My Future

For My Finances

My Truth for the Day

Date: ___/___/___

For Myself

For My Loved Ones

For My Community

For My Work

For My Future

For My Finances

My Truth for the Day

Date: ___/___/___

For Myself

For My Loved Ones

For My Community

For My Work

For My Future

For My Finances

My Truth for the Day

Date: ___/___/___

For Myself

For My Loved Ones

For My Community

For My Work

For My Future

For My Finances

My Truth for the Day

Date: ___/___/___

For Myself

For My Loved Ones

For My Community

For My Work

For My Future

For My Finances

My Truth for the Day

Date: ___/___/___

For Myself

For My Loved Ones

For My Community

For My Work

For My Future

For My Finances

My Truth for the Day

Date: ___/___/___

For Myself

For My Loved Ones

For My Community

For My Work

For My Future

For My Finances

My Truth for the Day

Date: ___/___/___

For Myself

For My Loved Ones

For My Community

For My Work

For My Future

For My Finances

My Truth for the Day

Date: ___/___/___

For Myself

For My Loved Ones

For My Community

For My Work

For My Future

For My Finances

My Truth for the Day

Date: ___/___/___

For Myself

For My Loved Ones

For My Community

For My Work

For My Future

For My Finances

My Truth for the Day

Date: ___/___/___

For Myself

For My Loved Ones

For My Community

For My Work

For My Future

For My Finances

My Truth for the Day

Date: ___/___/___

For Myself

For My Loved Ones

For My Community

For My Work

For My Future

For My Finances

My Truth for the Day

Date: ___/___/___

For Myself

For My Loved Ones

For My Community

For My Work

For My Future

For My Finances

My Truth for the Day

Date: ___/___/___

For Myself

For My Loved Ones

For My Community

For My Work

For My Future

For My Finances

My Truth for the Day

Date: ___/___/___

For Myself

For My Loved Ones

For My Community

For My Work

For My Future

For My Finances

My Truth for the Day

Date: ___/___/___

For Myself

For My Loved Ones

For My Community

For My Work

For My Future

For My Finances

My Truth for the Day

Date: ___/___/___

For Myself

For My Loved Ones

For My Community

For My Work

For My Future

For My Finances

My Truth for the Day

Date: ___/___/___

For Myself

For My Loved Ones

For My Community

For My Work

For My Future

For My Finances

My Truth for the Day

Date: ___/___/___

For Myself

For My Loved Ones

For My Community

For My Work

For My Future

For My Finances

My Truth for the Day

Date: ___/___/___

For Myself

For My Loved Ones

For My Community

For My Work

For My Future

For My Finances

My Truth for the Day

Date: ___/___/___

For Myself

For My Loved Ones

For My Community

For My Work

For My Future

For My Finances

My Truth for the Day

Date: ___/___/___

For Myself

For My Loved Ones

For My Community

For My Work

For My Future

For My Finances

My Truth for the Day

Date: ___/___/___

For Myself

For My Loved Ones

For My Community

For My Work

For My Future

For My Finances

My Truth for the Day

Date: ___/___/___

For Myself

For My Loved Ones

For My Community

For My Work

For My Future

For My Finances

My Truth for the Day

Date: ___/___/___

For Myself

For My Loved Ones

For My Community

For My Work

For My Future

For My Finances

My Truth for the Day

Date: ___/___/___

For Myself

For My Loved Ones

For My Community

For My Work

For My Future

For My Finances

My Truth for the Day

Date: ___/___/___

For Myself

For My Loved Ones

For My Community

For My Work

For My Future

For My Finances

My Truth for the Day

Date: ___/___/___

For Myself

For My Loved Ones

For My Community

For My Work

For My Future

For My Finances

My Truth for the Day

Date: ___/___/___

For Myself

For My Loved Ones

For My Community

For My Work

For My Future

For My Finances

My Truth for the Day

Date: ___/___/___

For Myself

For My Loved Ones

For My Community

For My Work

For My Future

For My Finances

My Truth for the Day

Date: ___/___/___

For Myself

For My Loved Ones

For My Community

For My Work

For My Future

For My Finances

My Truth for the Day

Date: ___/___/___

For Myself

For My Loved Ones

For My Community

For My Work

For My Future

For My Finances

My Truth for the Day

Date: ___/___/___

For Myself

For My Loved Ones

For My Community

For My Work

For My Future

For My Finances

My Truth for the Day

Date: ___/___/___

For Myself

For My Loved Ones

For My Community

For My Work

For My Future

For My Finances

My Truth for the Day

Date: ___/___/___

For Myself

For My Loved Ones

For My Community

For My Work

For My Future

For My Finances

My Truth for the Day

Date: ___/___/___

For Myself

For My Loved Ones

For My Community

For My Work

For My Future

For My Finances

My Truth for the Day

Date: ___/___/___

For Myself

For My Loved Ones

For My Community

For My Work

For My Future

For My Finances

My Truth for the Day

Date: ___/___/___

For Myself

For My Loved Ones

For My Community

For My Work

For My Future

For My Finances

My Truth for the Day

Date: ___/___/___

For Myself

For My Loved Ones

For My Community

For My Work

For My Future

For My Finances

My Truth for the Day

Date: ___/___/___

For Myself

For My Loved Ones

For My Community

For My Work

For My Future

For My Finances

My Truth for the Day

Date: ___/___/___

For Myself

For My Loved Ones

For My Community

For My Work

For My Future

For My Finances

My Truth for the Day

Date: ___/___/___

For Myself

For My Loved Ones

For My Community

For My Work

For My Future

For My Finances

My Truth for the Day

Date: ___/___/___

For Myself

For My Loved Ones

For My Community

For My Work

For My Future

For My Finances

My Truth for the Day

Date: ___/___/___

For Myself

For My Loved Ones

For My Community

For My Work

For My Future

For My Finances

My Truth for the Day

Date: ___/___/___

For Myself

For My Loved Ones

For My Community

For My Work

For My Future

For My Finances

My Truth for the Day

Date: ___/___/___

For Myself

For My Loved Ones

For My Community

For My Work

For My Future

For My Finances

My Truth for the Day

Date: ___/___/___

For Myself

For My Loved Ones

For My Community

For My Work

For My Future

For My Finances

My Truth for the Day

Date: ___/___/___

For Myself

For My Loved Ones

For My Community

For My Work

For My Future

For My Finances

My Truth for the Day

Date: ___/___/___

For Myself

For My Loved Ones

For My Community

For My Work

For My Future

For My Finances

My Truth for the Day

Date: ___/___/___

For Myself

For My Loved Ones

For My Community

For My Work

For My Future

For My Finances

My Truth for the Day

Date: ___/___/___

For Myself

For My Loved Ones

For My Community

For My Work

For My Future

For My Finances

My Truth for the Day

Date: ___/___/___

For Myself

For My Loved Ones

For My Community

For My Work

For My Future

For My Finances

My Truth for the Day

Date: ___/___/___

For Myself

For My Loved Ones

For My Community

For My Work

For My Future

For My Finances

My Truth for the Day

Date: ___/___/___

For Myself

For My Loved Ones

For My Community

For My Work

For My Future

For My Finances

My Truth for the Day

Date: ___/___/___

For Myself

For My Loved Ones

For My Community

For My Work

For My Future

For My Finances

My Truth for the Day

Date: ___/___/___

For Myself

For My Loved Ones

For My Community

For My Work

For My Future

For My Finances

My Truth for the Day

Date: ___/___/___

For Myself

For My Loved Ones

For My Community

For My Work

For My Future

For My Finances

My Truth for the Day

Date: ___/___/___

For Myself

For My Loved Ones

For My Community

For My Work

For My Future

For My Finances

My Truth for the Day

Date: ___/___/___

For Myself

For My Loved Ones

For My Community

For My Work

For My Future

For My Finances

My Truth for the Day

Date: ___/___/___

For Myself

For My Loved Ones

For My Community

For My Work

For My Future

For My Finances

My Truth for the Day

Date: ___/___/___

For Myself

For My Loved Ones

For My Community

For My Work

For My Future

For My Finances

My Truth for the Day

Date: ___/___/___

For Myself

For My Loved Ones

For My Community

For My Work

For My Future

For My Finances

My Truth for the Day

Date: ___/___/___

For Myself

For My Loved Ones

For My Community

For My Work

For My Future

For My Finances

My Truth for the Day

Date: ___/___/___

For Myself

For My Loved Ones

For My Community

For My Work

For My Future

For My Finances

My Truth for the Day

Date: ___/___/___

For Myself

For My Loved Ones

For My Community

For My Work

For My Future

For My Finances

My Truth for the Day

Date: ___/___/___

For Myself

For My Loved Ones

For My Community

For My Work

For My Future

For My Finances

My Truth for the Day

Date: ___/___/___

For Myself

For My Loved Ones

For My Community

For My Work

For My Future

For My Finances

My Truth for the Day

Date: ___/___/___

For Myself

For My Loved Ones

For My Community

For My Work

For My Future

For My Finances

My Truth for the Day

Date: ___/___/___

For Myself

For My Loved Ones

For My Community

For My Work

For My Future

For My Finances

My Truth for the Day

Date: ___/___/___

For Myself

For My Loved Ones

For My Community

For My Work

For My Future

For My Finances

My Truth for the Day

Date: ___/___/___

For Myself

For My Loved Ones

For My Community

For My Work

For My Future

For My Finances

My Truth for the Day

Date: ___/___/___

For Myself

For My Loved Ones

For My Community

For My Work

For My Future

For My Finances

My Truth for the Day

Date: ___/___/___

For Myself

For My Loved Ones

For My Community

For My Work

For My Future

For My Finances

My Truth for the Day

Date: ___/___/___

For Myself

For My Loved Ones

For My Community

For My Work

For My Future

For My Finances

My Truth for the Day

Date: ___/___/___

For Myself

For My Loved Ones

For My Community

For My Work

For My Future

For My Finances

My Truth for the Day

Date: ___/___/___

For Myself

For My Loved Ones

For My Community

For My Work

For My Future

For My Finances

My Truth for the Day

Date: ___/___/___

For Myself

For My Loved Ones

For My Community

For My Work

For My Future

For My Finances

My Truth for the Day

Date: ___/___/___

For Myself

For My Loved Ones

For My Community

For My Work

For My Future

For My Finances

My Truth for the Day

Made in the USA
Middletown, DE
14 September 2021